YPS/PCC

D0183470

Playgroup
Coll.

Opposites

For Tom Ellen

First published 1985 as *Bathwater's Hot* by Walker Books Ltd
87 Vauxhall Walk, London SE11 5HJ

This edition published 2016

2 4 6 8 10 9 7 5 3 1

© 1985 Shirley Hughes

The right of Shirley Hughes to be identified as author/illustrator of this work
has been asserted by her in accordance with the Copyright, Designs and Patents Act 1988

This book has been typeset in Plantin Light Educational

Printed in China

British Library Cataloguing in Publication Data:
a catalogue record for this book is available from the British Library

ISBN 978-1-4063-7279-3

www.walker.co.uk

THE NURSERY COLLECTION

OPPOSITES

WALKER BOOKS
AND SUBSIDIARIES
LONDON · BOSTON · SYDNEY · AUCKLAND

Bathwater's hot,

Seawater's cold,

Ginger's kittens are *very* young

But Buster's getting old.

Some things you can throw away,

Some are nice to keep.

Here's someone who is wide awake,

Shhh, he's fast asleep!

Some things are hard as stone,
Some are soft as cloud.

Whisper very quietly ...

SHOUT OUT LOUD!

It's fun to run very fast

Or to be slow.

The red light says "stop"

And the green light says "go".

It's kind to be helpful,

Unkind to tease,

Rather rude to push and grab,
Polite to say "please".

Night time is dark,

Day time is light.

The sun says "good morning"

And the moon says "good night".